Saxophone Exam Pieces

ABRSM Grade 3

Selected from the 2018–2021 syllabus

Name

Date of e

C000247191

Contents

page

Consultant Editor for ABRSM: David Blackwell
Footnotes: Anthony Burton

Other pieces for Grade 3

Alternative pieces for Eb and Bb saxophones are listed in the piano accompaniment booklet.

First published in 2017 by ABRSM (Publishing) Ltd,
a wholly owned subsidiary of ABRSM, 4 London Wall Place,
London EC2Y 5AU, United Kingdom
© 2017 by The Associated Board of the Royal Schools of Music
Distributed worldwide by Oxford University Press

Music origination by Julia Bovee
Cover by Kate Benjamin & Andy Potts
Printed in England by Halstan & Co. Ltd, Amersham, Bucks.,
on materials from sustainable sources.

Flower Duet

from *Lakmé*, Act I

Arranged by Alan Bullard

Léo Delibes
(1836–91)

The opera *Lakmé* was first produced in Paris in 1883, and is a tale of love and revenge set in 19th-century India. Its best-known song – thanks largely to its use in a 1980s television advertisement for British Airways – is the 'Flower Duet', sung by Lakmé, a priest's daughter, and her servant Mallika as they set out to gather flowers by a river. In this new arrangement of the main section of the duet, the two parallel vocal lines are played on the saxophone and the piano (right-hand part).

Tower Hill

Arranged by David Blackwell

Giles Farnaby
(c.1563–1640)

Giles Farnaby was a London composer of the Elizabethan and Jacobean eras, best known for writing miniature pieces for the virginal, a small harpsichord popular at the time. Most of these were preserved in the *Fitzwilliam Virginal Book*, which is thought to have been copied by or for a prisoner in a London jail between 1609 and 1619. Among them is *Tower Hill*, named after the area where the Tower of London stands. Each of its two 'strains', the first of four bars and the second of eight, is repeated in a varied and decorated form – in this arrangement, the variations begin as echoes.

My dear beloved

Caro mio ben

A:3

Arranged by David Sutton-Anderson

attrib. Giuseppe Giordani
(1751–98)

Caro mio ben (My dear beloved) is a love song in Italian, well known to generations of singers because of its inclusion in the popular anthology *Arie antiche*. It is usually said to be by Giuseppe Giordani, an opera composer from Naples in southern Italy – though it has also been attributed to Tommaso Giordani (*c*.1730-33–1806), another (unrelated) Neapolitan composer. The arranger's miniature cadenza at bar 19 and ornamentation of the melody from bar 25 to the end are the kind of decoration expected in vocal music of the later 18th century.

Foxtrot

B:1

Paul Harris

Paul Harris studied the clarinet, composition and conducting at the Royal Academy of Music in London, and has gone on to become a respected clarinet teacher, adjudicator and workshop leader, a prolific composer and an influential author on the subject of music education. This piece is in the rhythm of the foxtrot, a ballroom dance to syncopated music which was at its most popular in the 1930s.

© Copyright 1986 by Boosey & Hawkes Music Publishers Ltd
Reproduced from *Seven Easy Dances for Alto Saxophone and Piano* and *First Repertoire Pieces for Tenor Saxophone* by permission of Boosey & Hawkes Music Publishers Ltd.

Nocturne

No. 5 from *Rhythm & Rag*

Alan Haughton
(born 1950)

B:2

Alan Haughton is a British jazz and classical pianist, formerly a teacher, who has written a good deal of music for young performers, including the *Play Piano* series and the *Rhythm & Rag* jazz series for various instruments. However, this 'night piece' has no swung jazz rhythms: instead it is in the gentle $\frac{6}{8}$ metre of a lullaby, with correspondingly restrained dynamic markings.

© 2000 by The Associated Board of the Royal Schools of Music
Reproduced from Alan Haughton: *Rhythm & Rag for E flat Saxophone* and *Rhythm & Rag for B flat Saxophone* (ABRSM)

Saxophone Exam Pieces

ABRSM Grade 3

Selected from the 2018–2021 syllabus

Piano accompaniment for B♭ saxophones

Contents

page

LIST A

LIST B

Consultant Editor for ABRSM: David Blackwell
Footnotes: Anthony Burton

Other pieces for Grade 3

LIST A

LIST B

LIST C

Editorial guidance

We have taken the pieces in this book from a variety of sources. Where appropriate, we have edited the pieces to help you prepare for your performance. We have added metronome markings (in square brackets) and ornament realizations. Details of other changes or suggestions are given in the footnotes. These editorial additions are for guidance only: you do not have to follow them in the exam.

First published in 2017 by ABRSM (Publishing) Ltd,
a wholly owned subsidiary of ABRSM, 4 London Wall Place,
London EC2Y 5AU, United Kingdom
© 2017 by The Associated Board of the Royal Schools of Music
Distributed worldwide by Oxford University Press

Music origination by Julia Bovee
Cover by Kate Benjamin & Andy Potts
Printed in England by Halstan & Co. Ltd, Amersham, Bucks.,
on materials from sustainable sources.

Flower Duet

from *Lakmé*, Act I

Arranged by Alan Bullard

Léo Delibes
(1836–91)

The opera *Lakmé* was first produced in Paris in 1883, and is a tale of love and revenge set in 19th-century India. Its best-known song – thanks largely to its use in a 1980s television advertisement for British Airways – is the 'Flower Duet', sung by Lakmé, a priest's daughter, and her servant Mallika as they set out to gather flowers by a river. In this new arrangement of the main section of the duet, the two parallel vocal lines are played on the saxophone and the piano (right-hand part).

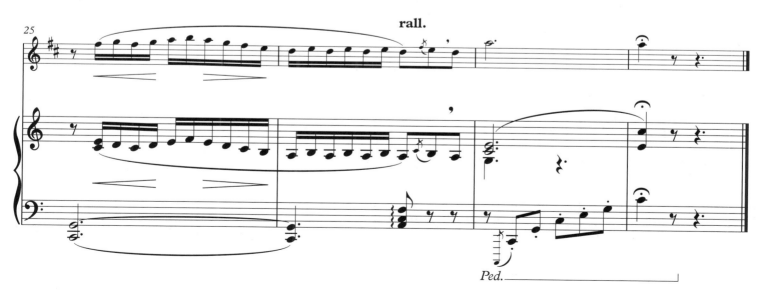

Bb piano accompaniment

Tower Hill

A:2

Arranged by David Blackwell

Giles Farnaby
(c.1563–1640)

Giles Farnaby was a London composer of the Elizabethan and Jacobean eras, best known for writing miniature pieces for the virginal, a small harpsichord popular at the time. Most of these were preserved in the *Fitzwilliam Virginal Book*, which is thought to have been copied by or for a prisoner in a London jail between 1609 and 1619. Among them is *Tower Hill*, named after the area where the Tower of London stands. Each of its two 'strains', the first of four bars and the second of eight, is repeated in a varied and decorated form – in this arrangement, the variations begin as echoes.

My dear beloved

Caro mio ben

Arranged by David Sutton-Anderson

attrib. Giuseppe Giordani
(1751–98)

Caro mio ben (My dear beloved) is a love song in Italian, well known to generations of singers because of its inclusion in the popular anthology *Arie antiche*. It is usually said to be by Giuseppe Giordani, an opera composer from Naples in southern Italy – though it has also been attributed to Tommaso Giordani (*c*.1730-33–1806), another (unrelated) Neapolitan composer. The arranger's miniature cadenza at bar 19 and ornamentation of the melody from bar 25 to the end are the kind of decoration expected in vocal music of the later 18th century.

B:1

Foxtrot

Paul Harris

Paul Harris studied the clarinet, composition and conducting at the Royal Academy of Music in London, and has gone on to become a respected clarinet teacher, adjudicator and workshop leader, a prolific composer and an influential author on the subject of music education. This piece is in the rhythm of the foxtrot, a ballroom dance to syncopated music which was at its most popular in the 1930s.

Nocturne

No. 5 from *Rhythm & Rag*

Alan Haughton
(born 1950)

B:2

Alan Haughton is a British jazz and classical pianist, formerly a teacher, who has written a good deal of music for young performers, including the *Play Piano* series and the *Rhythm & Rag* jazz series for various instruments. However, this 'night piece' has no swung jazz rhythms: instead it is in the gentle $\frac{6}{8}$ metre of a lullaby, with correspondingly restrained dynamic markings.

© 2000 by The Associated Board of the Royal Schools of Music
Reproduced from Alan Haughton: *Rhythm & Rag for B flat Saxophone* (ABRSM)

B:3

Bye Bye Blackbird

Arranged by Ned Bennett

Words by Mort Dixon (1892–1956)
Music by Ray Henderson (1896–1970)

'Bye Bye Blackbird' is a popular song of the 1920s, with lyrics and music by two of the most successful songwriters of the time. It has become a jazz 'standard', a tune widely used as a basis for improvisation. In the song, a traveller says goodbye to the 'blackbird' of unhappiness as he or she approaches the happy ending of a journey. This arrangement features the chorus: the words 'Bye bye blackbird' are sung to the notes in bars 9–12 and 17–20, and 'Blackbird, bye bye' to bars 33–35 and 49–52.

10

Phish and Chips

Karen Street
(born 1959)

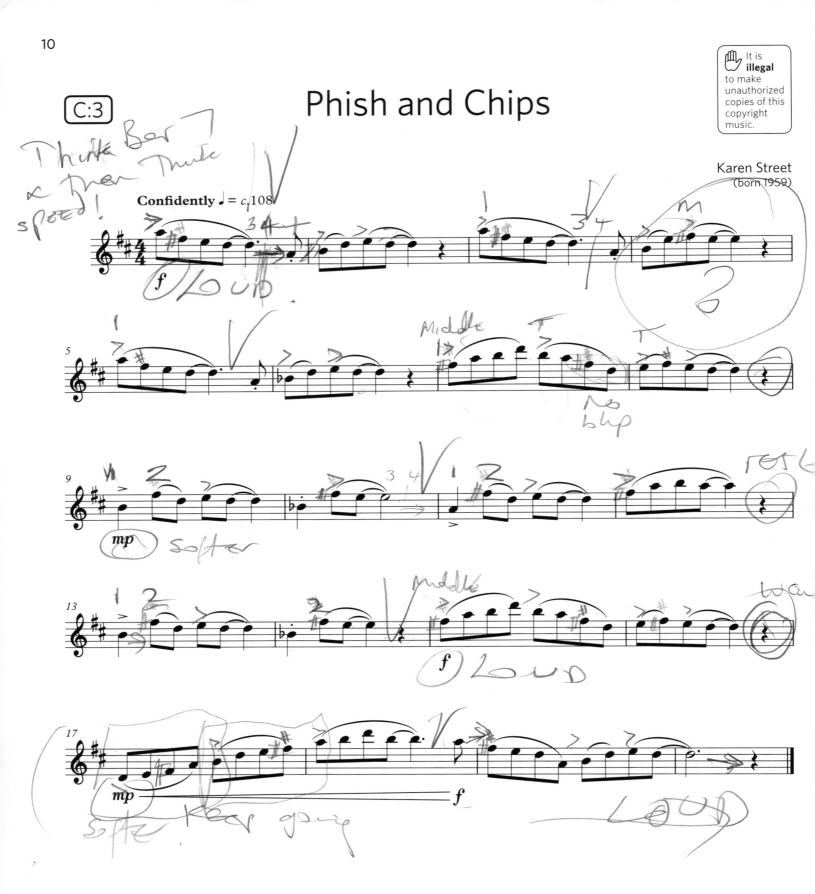

Karen Street is a well-known player of the accordion and the saxophone. Early in her career, she played both instruments in Mike Westbrook's jazz band; later, she was a member of the all-female saxophone quartet The Fairer Sax. She has written a great deal of music for both her instruments. She collaborated with two other composers on *Double Click!!*, a collection of 30 'byte-size pieces' for solo saxophone with computer-related titles. Chris Gumbley, the compiler of the volume, says that *Phish and Chips* 'should have a cheerful and jaunty character. Lightly accent the first beat of each bar, and don't be tempted to swing the quavers.'

© Gumbles Publications 2012
Taken from *Double Click!!* (Rae/Street/Gumbley) for Solo Saxophone. The book and a backing track are available from gumblespublications.co.uk (the backing track should not be used in the exam).

AB 3873

Andante in B minor

from *Practische Flötenschule*, Op. 53

Edited by David Blackwell

Heinrich Soussmann
(1796–1848)

Heinrich Soussmann was a German flautist who played in an army band as a teenager, and later became principal flautist of the opera orchestra at St Petersburg, then the Russian capital. This piece is from his four-volume *Practical Flute Tutor*, which was published in the 1840s (the decade in which the saxophone was invented). It needs graceful articulation in both the legato and staccato phrases.

Source: *Practische Flötenschule in 4 cahiers*, Op. 53 (Hamburg, [1845?]). This piece has been newly edited for saxophone and all dynamics are editorial. In some other editions the D♯ in b. 9 is written as D♮.

© 2017 by The Associated Board of the Royal Schools of Music

C:1

Driving Sax

No. 26 from *Sixty for Sax*

Alan Bullard
(born 1947)

Alan Bullard was for many years Head of Composition at Colchester Institute (in south-east England) and is now a full-time composer. He is well known for his Christmas carols and his music for schools and young performers. He has written frequently for saxophone, the instrument played professionally by his son, Sam. This piece, in a 'driving' 4/4 time with equal quavers, requires percussive attacks and a strong sense of rhythm (as if a drummer were playing along with it).

Bye Bye Blackbird

B:3

Arranged by Ned Bennett

Words by Mort Dixon (1892–1956)
Music by Ray Henderson (1896–1970)

'Bye Bye Blackbird' is a popular song of the 1920s, with lyrics and music by two of the most successful songwriters of the time. It has become a jazz 'standard', a tune widely used as a basis for improvisation. In the song, a traveller says goodbye to the 'blackbird' of unhappiness as he or she approaches the happy ending of a journey. This arrangement features the chorus: the words 'Bye bye blackbird' are sung to the notes in bars 9–12 and 17–20, and 'Blackbird, bye bye' to bars 33–35 and 49–52.

Saxophone Exam Pieces

ABRSM Grade 3

Selected from the 2018–2021 syllabus

Piano accompaniment for E♭ saxophones

Contents

Consultant Editor for ABRSM: David Blackwell
Footnotes: Anthony Burton

Other pieces for Grade 3

Editorial guidance

We have taken the pieces in this book from a variety of sources. Where appropriate, we have edited the pieces to help you prepare for your performance. We have added metronome markings (in square brackets) and ornament realizations. Details of other changes or suggestions are given in the footnotes. These editorial additions are for guidance only: you do not have to follow them in the exam.

First published in 2017 by ABRSM (Publishing) Ltd,
a wholly owned subsidiary of ABRSM, 4 London Wall Place,
London EC2Y 5AU, United Kingdom
© 2017 by The Associated Board of the Royal Schools of Music
Distributed worldwide by Oxford University Press

Music origination by Julia Bovee
Cover by Kate Benjamin & Andy Potts
Printed in England by Halstan & Co. Ltd, Amersham, Bucks.,
on materials from sustainable sources.

Flower Duet

from *Lakmé*, Act I

Arranged by Alan Bullard

A:1

Léo Delibes
(1836–91)

The opera *Lakmé* was first produced in Paris in 1883, and is a tale of love and revenge set in 19th-century India. Its best-known song – thanks largely to its use in a 1980s television advertisement for British Airways – is the 'Flower Duet', sung by Lakmé, a priest's daughter, and her servant Mallika as they set out to gather flowers by a river. In this new arrangement of the main section of the duet, the two parallel vocal lines are played on the saxophone and the piano (right-hand part).

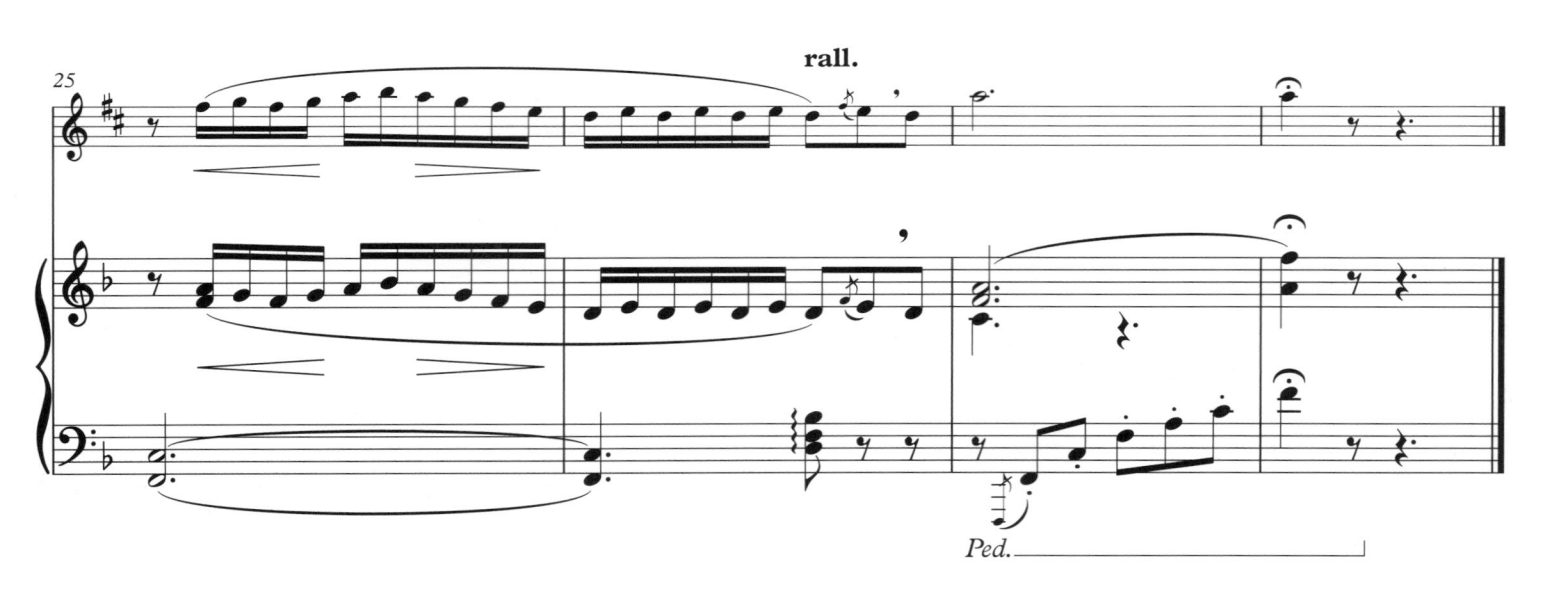

Tower Hill

Arranged by David Blackwell

Giles Farnaby
(c.1563–1640)

Giles Farnaby was a London composer of the Elizabethan and Jacobean eras, best known for writing miniature pieces for the virginal, a small harpsichord popular at the time. Most of these were preserved in the *Fitzwilliam Virginal Book*, which is thought to have been copied by or for a prisoner in a London jail between 1609 and 1619. Among them is *Tower Hill*, named after the area where the Tower of London stands. Each of its two 'strains', the first of four bars and the second of eight, is repeated in a varied and decorated form – in this arrangement, the variations begin as echoes.

© 2017 by The Associated Board of the Royal Schools of Music

My dear beloved

Caro mio ben

Arranged by David Sutton-Anderson

attrib. Giuseppe Giordani
(1751–98)

Caro mio ben (My dear beloved) is a love song in Italian, well known to generations of singers because of its inclusion in the popular anthology *Arie antiche*. It is usually said to be by Giuseppe Giordani, an opera composer from Naples in southern Italy – though it has also been attributed to Tommaso Giordani (*c.*1730-33–1806), another (unrelated) Neapolitan composer. The arranger's miniature cadenza at bar 19 and ornamentation of the melody from bar 25 to the end are the kind of decoration expected in vocal music of the later 18th century.

Eb piano accompaniment

Foxtrot

Paul Harris

Allegro spiritoso [♩ = c.126]

Paul Harris studied the clarinet, composition and conducting at the Royal Academy of Music in London, and has gone on to become a respected clarinet teacher, adjudicator and workshop leader, a prolific composer and an influential author on the subject of music education. This piece is in the rhythm of the foxtrot, a ballroom dance to syncopated music which was at its most popular in the 1930s.

B:2

Nocturne

No. 5 from *Rhythm & Rag*

Alan Haughton
(born 1950)

Andante cantabile [♩. = *c*.44]

con Ped.

Alan Haughton is a British jazz and classical pianist, formerly a teacher, who has written a good deal of music for young performers, including the *Play Piano* series and the *Rhythm & Rag* jazz series for various instruments. However, this 'night piece' has no swung jazz rhythms: instead it is in the gentle $\frac{6}{8}$ metre of a lullaby, with correspondingly restrained dynamic markings.

© 2000 by The Associated Board of the Royal Schools of Music
Reproduced from Alan Haughton: *Rhythm & Rag for E flat Saxophone* (ABRSM)

Eb piano accompaniment

Bye Bye Blackbird

Arranged by Ned Bennett

Words by Mort Dixon (1892–1956)
Music by Ray Henderson (1896–1970)

'Bye Bye Blackbird' is a popular song of the 1920s, with lyrics and music by two of the most successful songwriters of the time. It has become a jazz 'standard', a tune widely used as a basis for improvisation. In the song, a traveller says goodbye to the 'blackbird' of unhappiness as he or she approaches the happy ending of a journey. This arrangement features the chorus: the words 'Bye bye blackbird' are sung to the notes in bars 9–12 and 17–20, and 'Blackbird, bye bye' to bars 33–35 and 49–52.